52
SACRED SONGS
YOU LIKE TO SING

G. SCHIRMER, Inc.

DISTRIBUTED BY

HAL•LEONARD®
CORPORATION
7777 W. BLUEMOUND RD. P.O. BOX 13819 MILWAUKEE, WI 53213

). 1642

INDEX BY COMPOSER

INDEX BY TITLE

Agnus Dei.

(Lamb of God.)

(Mezzo-Soprano, or Baritone.)

GEORGES BIZET.

A — gnus De — i! qui tol- lis pec-ca- ta mun - di,
Lamb___ of God, thou that tak-est a-way the world's guilt,

"And God shall wipe away all tears:"

from "The Light of the World."

Andante moderato.

ARTHUR SULLIVAN.

The Lord is ris - en, He will dwell with men, and they shall be his— peo - ple! And God shall wipe a - way all tears from their eyes, There shall be no more death, neith - er sor - row nor cry - ing, neith - er—

shall there be__ an - y more pain. God shall wipe a - way all

tears from their eyes: There shall be no more death, neith - er sor - row nor

cry - ing, neith - er__ shall there be__ an - y more pain, For the

form - er things are pass'd a - way. Be - hold, I make all things

new, Saith the Lord, For the form-er things are pass'd a - way. Be - hold, I make

all things new, Saith the Lord, Saith the Lord.

God shall wipe a - way all tears from their eyes, There shall be

no more death, neith-er sor - row nor cry - ing, neith - er

Arise, O Lord

Adapted from Psalm IX

Leon Abbott Hoffmeister

wick - ed be turn - ed in - to hell, the wick - ed be turn - ed in - to hell, e - ven the na - tions, that for - get___ God, the na - tions that for-get God. Put them in fear, in fear, O Lord: let the na - tions know them-selves to be but men.

Slightly slower

For they that know thy name will put their trust in thee. And thou, Lord, wilt not, wilt not for-sake them. For they that know thy name will

Arm, arm, ye brave.

Recit. and Aria from "Judas Maccabaeus."

Edited by H. HEALE.

G. F. HÄNDEL.

ear; and points out Mac-ca-bae-us to their aid. Ju-das shall set the cap-tive

free, And lead us on to vic-to-ry!

Allegro.

Arm, arm ye brave!

Arm, arm ye brave! a no-ble cause, a no-ble cause,

The cause of Heav'n your zeal demands, a

no- -ble cause, The cause of Heav'n your zeal de-mands, a

no- -ble cause, The cause of Heav'n your zeal de-mands.

Arm, arm ye brave!

Arm, arm ye brave! a no-ble cause,   Arm, arm,

arm, arm, ye brave! arm, arm, arm, arm, ye brave! a no-ble cause, The

cause of Heav'n, your zeal de-mands, a no-ble cause, Arm, arm, ye brave! a

no-ble cause, The cause of Heav'n your zeal demands,   arm,

arm, The cause of Heav'n your zeal de-mands.

In de - fence of your na - tion, re - li - gion, and laws, Th'al -

might - y Je - ho - vah will strength - en your hands; In de -

fence of your na - tion, re - li - gion, and laws,

Th'al - might - y Je - ho - vah will strength - - - -

Art Thou the Christ?

Daniel S. Twohig*

Geoffrey O'Hara

* Poem used by permission

thou be Christ, then save Thy-self; Come down from the cross, now."— But

Je - sus prayed: "Fa-ther for-give, for they know not what they do",____ And to the

thief He said: "in Par-a-dise, This day Thou shalt be with me too".____ "Art

Thou the Christ?" they asked Him.— Ah! fools that we should doubt, For to-

non legato

day from ev - 'ry house - top, His mes - sage thun - ders

r. h.

out, From o - cean, moun - tain, val - ley, From

To the Community Welfare Associations

Because of Thy Great Bounty

Grace Noll Crowell*

Leon A. Hoffmeister

*Words used by permission of Grace Noll Crowell

Each day I live I shall di-vide my gifts from Thee With

ev - 'ry broth-er that I see Who has the need of help from

me, the need of help from me. Be -

cause I have been shel-tered, fed By Thy good care,

Ave Maria

Original poem by
Sir Walter Scott

German translation by
Adam Stork

English adaptation by
Dr. Theo. Baker

Franz Schubert, Op. 52, No. 6

wild,   'Tis Thou, 'tis Thou canst save a - mid _____ de-spair.   We
wild   *soll mein Ge - bet zu dir hin-we - - hen.*   *Wir*
na,   A - ve, ____ A - ve! Do - mi - nus, Do - mi - nus te-cum.   Be-ne-

slum - ber safe-ly till the mor - row,   Tho' e'en by men out-cast, re-vil'd: O
schla - fen si-cher bis zum Mor - gen,   *ob Men - schen noch so grausam sind.*   *O*
di - cta tu in mu-li-e-ri-bus,   et be - ne - di - - ctus,   et

Maid - en, see a maid-en's sor-row,   O Moth - er, hear a suppliant child!
Jung - frau, sieh' der Jung-frau Sor-gen,   *o Mut - ter, hör' ein bit-tend Kind!*
be - ne - di - ctus fru - ctus ven-tris,   ven-tris tu - i, Je - - sus.

fp   *pp*

A - - - ve Ma - ri - -
A - - - *ve Ma - ri* - -
A - - - ve Ma - ri - -

I can-not see an-oth-er's lack And I not share My glow-ing fire, my loaf of bread, My roof's safe shel-ter o-ver-head, That he, too, may be com-fort-ed, be com-fort-ed.

Be-cause love has been lav-ished so Up-

on me, Lord, A wealth I know that was not meant For me to hoard, I shall give love to all I see, To all who need my sym-pa-thy. Thus shall I show my thanks to Thee, my thanks to Thee.

Be Near Me Still

Prayer

English version by
Alma Strettell

Ferd. Hiller. Op. 46

Moderato

Voice / Piano

Lord! in my heart's love deep I hide Thee, Be near me
Herr! den ich tief im Her - zen tra - ge, sei du mit

still! Thou tow'r of strength, what-e'er be - tide me, Be Thou with
mir, du Gna - den - hort in Glück und Pla - ge, sei du mit

me. Oh be my guard in life's bright plac - es, Lest pride pre - vail, When
mir. Be - hü - te mich am Born der Freu - de vor Ü - ber - muth, und

my pow'r un - shak - en, My soul's true sun, _____
du mei - ne Stär - ke, mein Son - nen - licht, _____

Till earth's dark days shall be for - sak - en, Be near me
bis an das En - de mei - ner Ta - ge, sei du mit

still! be near me still! Till earth's dark days shall be for -
mir, sei du mit mir, bis an das En - de mei - ner

sak - en, Be near me, near me still! _____
Ta - ge, sei du mit mir, mit mir. _____

Calvary

Word by HENRY VAUGHAN   *(For Mezzo-Soprano or Baritone)*   PAUL RODNEY

The pil - grims throng thro' the cit - y gates While the night is fall - ing fast; They go to watch on Cal - v'ry's hill Ere the twi - light hours __ are

Andante.

"Rest, rest to the wea - ry, Peace, peace to the soul;— Though life may be

drear - y, Earth is not thy goal.— O lay down thy bur - den,

O come un - to Me,— I will not for - sake thee, I will not for-

sake thee, I will not for - sake thee, Though all else should flee."—

Giubiloso.

Far, far a-way, o'er the dream __ of years, They hear the Voice of the King: __ "Where, O Grave, where is thy vic - - to-ry, And where, O Death, is __ thy sting?" __ Cap - tive He leads them for ev - - er-more, __ While

wea - ry pil - grims re - joice; _____ For look - ing on high to the

Cross He bore, ___ The faith - ful shall hear His Voice, _____ the

faith - ful shall hear His Voice: _____

Andante.
p con espress.

"Rest, rest to the wea - ry, Peace, peace to the soul; ___

Though life may be drear - y, Earth is not thy goal.___ O lay down thy

bur - den, O come un - to Me,___ I will not for - sake thee,

I will not for - sake thee, I will not for - sake thee, Though all else should

flee, though all else should flee."___

Cantique de Noël
Christmas Song

Edited by Carl Deis

Adolphe Adam

O ho - ly night!__ the stars are bright-ly
Mi - nuit,__ Chré - tien,__ c'est l'heu - re so - len-

shin - ing, It is the night of the dear Sav-iour's birth; Long lay the
nel - le Où l'Hom-me-Dieu des-cen-dit jus-qu'à nous, Pour ef-fa-

world in sin and er-ror pin - ing, Till he ap-pear'd, and the soul felt its worth. A
cer__ la tache o-ri-gi-nel - le Et de son père ar - rê-ter le cour-roux. Le

thrill of hope the wear-y world re-joi-ces, For yon-der breaks a new and glo-rious morn.
mon-de en-tier tres-sail-le d'es - pé-ran - ce A cet - te nuit qui lui donne un sau-veur.

Fall_____ on your knees!_____ oh hear_____ the an-gel voi - ces! O
Peu - ple, à ge - noux!_____ at - tends_____ ta dé-li-vran - ce. No-

night_____ di - vine!_____ O night_____ when Christ was born,_____ O
ël!_____ No - ël!_____ voi-ci_____ le Ré - demp-teur,_____ No-

night_____ di - vine!_____ O night, O_____ night di - vine.
ël!_____ No - ël!_____ voi - ci le_____ Ré-demp-teur.

Led by the
De no - tre

light__ of Faith se-rene-ly beam - ing, With glow-ing hearts by his cra - dle we stand;
foi__ que la lumière ar-den - te nous gui-de tous au ber-ceau de l'en-fant,

So, led by light of a star sweet-ly gleam - ing, Here came the wise men from__ the O-rient
comme au-tre-fois une é-toi-le bril-lan - te y con-dui-sit les chefs__ de l'o-ri-

land. The King of Kings lay thus in low-ly man-ger, In all our tri-als
ent. Le Roi des Rois naît dans une hum-ble crè - che; puis-sants du jour, fiers

46

Lord, then ev-er, ev-er praise we, His pow'r_____ and
bout, chan - te ta dé-li-vran - ce, No - ël!_____ No-

glo - ry__ ev - er-more pro - claim,_____ His pow'r_____ and
ël!_____ chan - tons_____ le Ré - demp - teur,_____ No - ël!_____ No-

Ossia:

glo - ry ev - er - more_____ pro - claim.
ël!_____ chan - tons le_____ Ré - demp - teur.

Christ be with me!

Text (adapted) attributed to
St. Patrick

Frédéric Chopin
Arranged by Carl Deis

Come to me

Adapted from
Matthew: XI, 28-30

Ludwig van Beethoven, Op. **27**, No. **2**
Adapted by Alexander Aslanoff

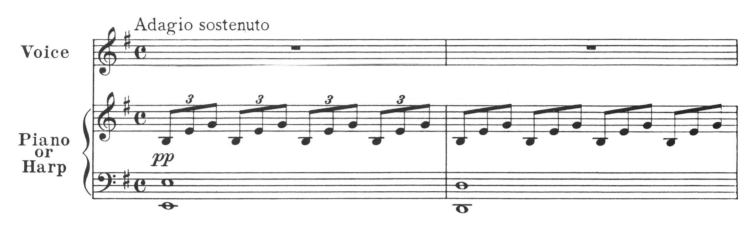

rest._____ Take my yoke, take my yoke up - on you and learn of me._____ All ye that la - bor, all ye that are heav - y - la - den:

heart.

pp *cresc.*

dim. *p*

decresc. *pp*

Come to

me, Come to me all ye that need rest.____ Come to

To my dear ones

Communion Hymn

Words and Music by
Mary Pickens Opie

Copyright, 1929, by G. Schirmer Inc.

That I may ev - er Dwell with-in Thy light, And come be-

fore Thee Stain-less, pure, and white.

Je - sus, my Sa - vior, Look with lov-ing eye

As from my heart I make this hum-ble cry.

Give of Thy-self, Dear Lord, that I may be

Filled with Thy grace, Through-out e-ter-ni-ty. A-men.

rit.

rit.

p

Crossing the Bar.

Poem by
LORD TENNYSON.

(Mezzo - Soprano, or Baritone.)

Music by
DUDLEY BUCK.

Twi-light and ev'n-ing bell, And af-ter that the

tranquillo.

dark: And may there be no sad-ness of fare-

well When I _____ em - bark; For

Crucifixus

English version by
F. W. Rosier

J. Faure

Vous qui pleu - rez, ve - nez à ce Dieu: car il pleu - re,
Come un - to Him, all ye who weep; for He too weep - eth.

Vous qui souf - frez, ve - nez à lui: car il gué - rit.
Come un - to Him, all ye who mourn; for He can heal.

sostenuto

Vous qui pleu - rez, _____ ve - nez à ce Dieu: car il pleu - - re,
Come un - to Him, _____ all ye who weep; for He too weep - - eth.

Vous qui souf - frez, ve - nez à lui: car il gué - rit.
Come un - to Him, all ye who mourn; for He can heal.

Vous qui tremblez, ve - nez à lui, _____
Come un - to Him, all ye who fear, _____

Evening and Morning
Sacred Song

Max Spicker. Op. 56

when___ the twi - light___ deep - ens in the grove, the___

twi - light deep - ens in the grove.

Comes___ at length a

sound of man - y voic - es, As when the waves break

light - ly on the shore; As when at dawn the feath-er'd choir re-

joic - es, Sing - ing a - loud,

sing - ing a - loud, _____ sing - ing a - loud, be - cause the night is

o'er.

voice of thrill-ing glad - ness, Borne on the breez-es of __ the

ris - - ing day, Say - ing, "The Lord shall

mf *cresc.* *poco* *a* *poco*

make an end of sad - ness, The Lord shall wipe all __ tears __ a-way, the __

f con calore *rall.* *ten.*

col canto

Lord shall wipe all tears __ a - way."

dim. *poco* *a* *poco* *rall.*

dim.

p rall.

dolce

Eye hath not seen

from the cantata "The Holy City"

Alfred Robert Gaul

the things which God hath pre-pared, pre - pared for them that_ love

Him.

Più mosso ♩=88

For He hath pre - pared_ for them_ a cit - y, whose

build - er and mak - er is God, He hath pre - pared,_ pre-

To my good friend, Arthur Kraft

God shall wipe away all tears

Revelation 21: 3, 4

Rob Roy Peery

Più mosso

and he will dwell with

them,   and they shall be his peo - ple,   he will dwell with them,   and

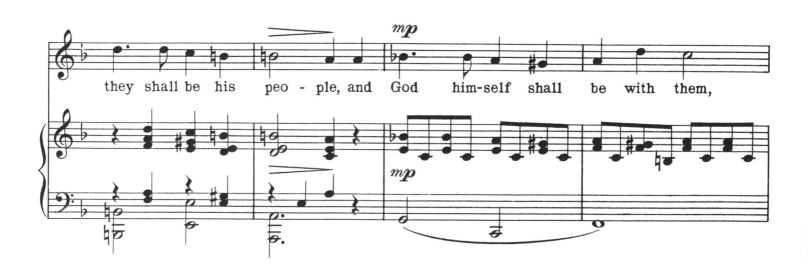

they shall be his peo - ple, and God him-self shall be with them,

God him-self shall be with them, he shall be their God, ____ shall

be their God.

And God shall wipe a-way all

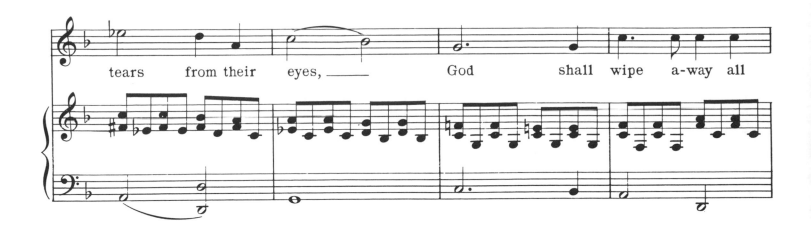

tears   from their   eyes, _____   God   shall   wipe   a-way   all

pp

tears   from   their   eyes; _____   and   there   shall   be   no   more

death,   nei-ther   sor - - row,   nor   cry - - ing,   nei-ther

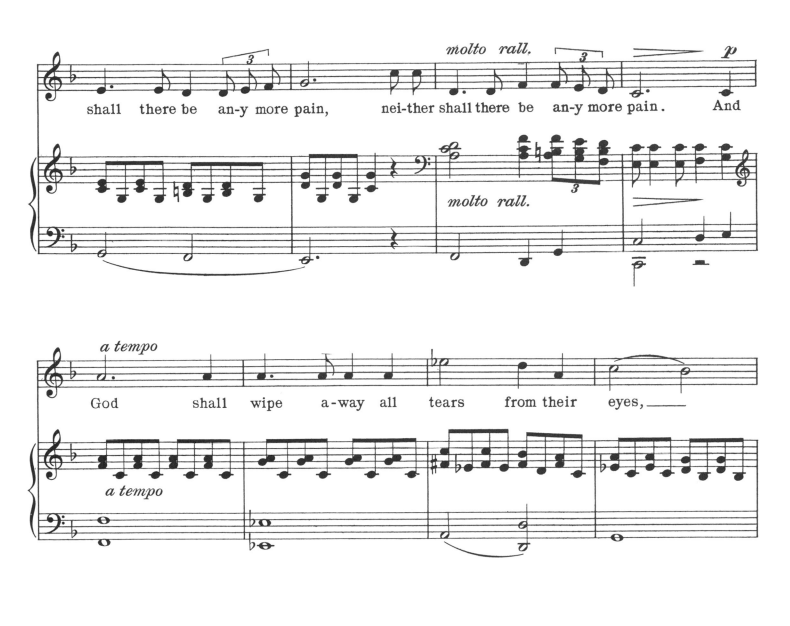

shall there be an-y more pain, nei-ther shall there be an-y more pain. And

a tempo

God shall wipe a-way all tears from their eyes,

God shall wipe a-way all tears from their eyes; and

He shall feed His flock

Recitative and Aria from "The Messiah"

Edited by Carl Deis

George Frideric Handel

Original conclusion of the Alto Solo

young.

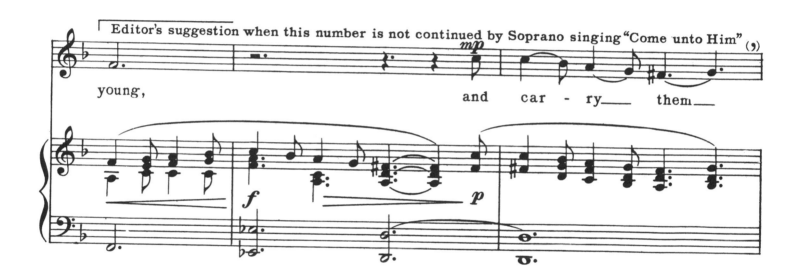

Editor's suggestion when this number is not continued by Soprano singing "Come unto Him"

young,

and car - ry___ them___

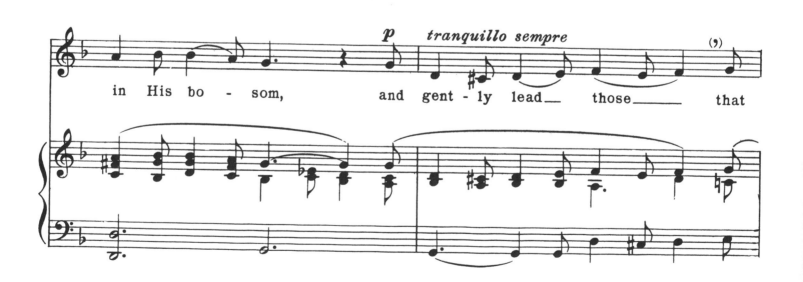

in His bo - som,

and gent - ly lead___ those___ that

are___ with young,___ and gent - ly lead,___ and gent - ly lead those_ that

dolce

are___ with young.

"He that keepeth Israel"

Sacred Song

Mezzo-Soprano or Baritone

ADOLPHE SCHLÖSSER

He that keep - eth Is - ra - el, slum - bers not, nor

sleeps,_____ He that keep - eth Is - ra - el,

slum - bers not, nor sleeps. He will give his An - gels

charge ov-er thee, To keep thee in all thy ways, in all thy ways,

He that keep - eth Is - ra - el, He that keep - eth

Is - ra - el, slum - bers not, nor sleeps.

Put thy trust in Him ___ and call up - on Him,   Put thy

trust   in   Him,   and call   up - on Him, for His ears   are

o - pen un - to   thy pray'rs; for His   ears   are   o - pen un -

to   thy pray'rs. ___

Hold Thou My Hand

Words and music by
Pearl G. Curran

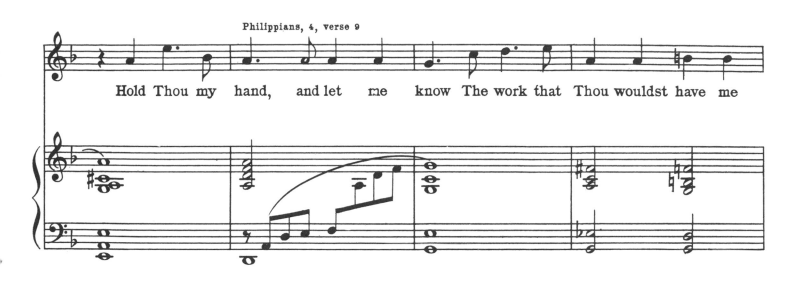

Philippians, 4, verse 9

Hold Thou my hand, and let me know The work that Thou wouldst have me

tranquillo Philippians, 4, verse 8

do; And ev-'ry hour may I be true_____ To those I love, dear God, a - bove,

Corinthians (i), 16, verse 13

Hold Thou my hand.

Should the way seem dark to

me   Then, dear Fa - ther, ___   let me be   All the stronger, faithful still;

Peter (ii), 1, verse 19

cresc.   *poco rall.*   *a tempo*

Hold   Thou my   hand, dear God, un-til   The dark hours pass, ___

John (i), 4, verse 16

and glo-rious light ___   Of Thy great Love ___

dawns on my sight; Then I'll clear - ly un - der-stand, And live with-in this

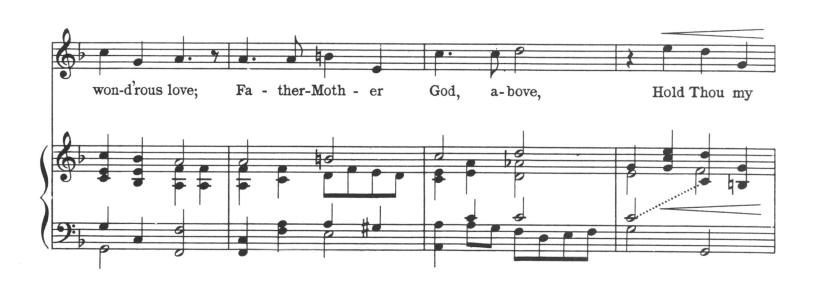

won-d'rous love; Fa - ther-Moth - er God, a-bove, Hold Thou my

hand, Then I'll clear - ly un - der-stand And live with-in this won-d'rous Love,

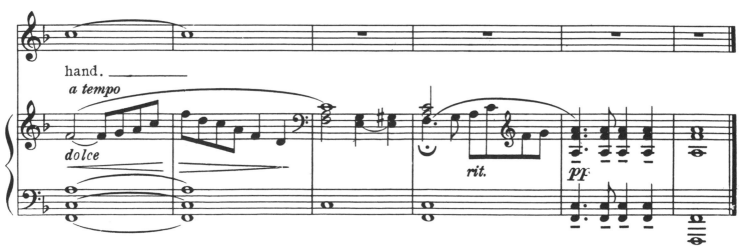

"Honor and arms."

Air from the Oratorio

"Samson."

G. F. Handel.

such a foe, scorn such__ a foe, Though I could

end thee at a blow, though I could end thee at a blow, though

I__ could end thee__ at__ a__ blow, Poor vic - to - ry,

to con - quer thee, Or glo - - - - - -

- - - - - -ry in____ thy o - ver-throw!

Hon - or and arms _____ scorn such a foe, scorn such __ a foe,

Though I could end thee at a blow, though I could

end thee at a blow, Poor vic - -to - ry, to con - -quer

thee, poor vic - to-ry, to con - quer thee, Or glo - - - - -

Fine.

Van-quish a slave that is half slain! So mean a tri - umph I dis-dain, so

mean a tri - -umph I dis-dain,_____ I dis-dain!

Van-quish a slave that is half slain! So mean____ a tri - - -

- - -umph I dis-dain,_____ so

I dis - dain, I dis-dain, so

mean a tri - umph, so mean a tri - umph I dis-dain,

so mean a tri - umph I dis-dain!

Hosanna!
EASTER SONG
(Julien Didiée)

English version by
N.H. DOLE

Jules Granier

Un poco più lento

Night, like_ a pall, seem'd to dis-pel the day, When God's dear
La som-bre nuit Voi-lait en-co- -re Du fils de

Son pass'd from the world a- way, But now on high beams pur-est
Dieu La sainte au-ro- -re, Mais le so-leil A res-plen-

light, Cre- a- tion bows_ o-verawed at the sight!_
di, Et l'u- ni- vers_ Se prosterne é-blou-i._

Recitative and Aria for Tenor
from
Elijah.

F. MENDELSSOHN.

Ye peo - ple, rend your hearts, rend your hearts, and not your garments; for your transgressions the Prophet E - li - jah hath seal - ed the Heavens through the word of God. I therefore say to ye, For - sake your i - dols, re - turn to God; for He is slow to an - ger, and mer - ci - ful, and kind, and gra - cious, and re - pent - eth Him of the e - vil.

find Him! "If with all your hearts ye tru-ly seek me, ye shall ev-er sure-ly find me."

Thus saith our God, "Ye shall ev-er sure-ly find me."

Thus saith our God.

"I heard the voice of Jesus say."

CHARLES A. E. HARRISS.

viv'd,___ And now I live in Him,___ and now I

live in Him,___ and now I live, I live in

Him, and now I live,_____ I live___

in Him.

I know that my Redeemer liveth

from the "Messiah"

Job 19: 25, 26; I Cor. 15: 20

George Frideric Handel

God, yet in my flesh__ shall I__ see God.

I know that my Re - deem - er liv - eth. and though

worms de - stroy this bod - y, yet in my flesh__ shall I see

God, yet in my flesh_____ shall I see God, shall I see

God. I know that my Re - deem - er liv - eth.

For now is Christ ris - en from the dead, the

first - - fruits of them that sleep, _____ of

them that sleep, the first - - fruits of them__ that sleep.

For now is Christ ris - en, for now is Christ

ris - en from the dead, the first___ fruits___

Adagio

of them that sleep.

I'm a Pilgrim

Mary S. B. Dana

Herbert Johnson

Where the life is fair and bright. ___ There the glo - ry ___ is ev-er

shin - ing, Oh my long-ing heart, my long-ing heart is there. ___ Here in this

coun-try ___ so dark and drea-ry. ___ Too long I've wandered, sad and wea - ry.

"It is enough."

Aria from Elijah.

F. Mendelssohn.

It is e - nough! O Lord, now take a-way my

life,___ for I am not bet - ter than my fa - thers.

It is e - nough! it is e - nough! Now

take a-way my life,__ I am not bet-ter, not bet- - -ter than my fa- - -thers, I am not bet-ter, I am not bet - ter than my fa - - -thers.

I de - sire__ to live no long-er; now let me die, for my days are but

"Jerusalem! Thou that killest the Prophets."

Aria for Soprano

from

St. Paul.

F. MENDELSSOHN.

thee!
sandt!

How of-ten would I have
Wie oft hab' ich nicht dei-ne

ga-ther'd un-to Me thy chil-dren, and ye would
Kin - der ver-sam-meln wol-len! und ihr habt nicht ge-

not, and ye would not!
wollt! und ihr habt nicht ge-wollt!

Lead, kindly Light

Sacred Song

(Soprano, or Tenor)

Words by the
Rev. JOHN HENRY NEWMAN

Music by
CIRO PINSUTI

Larghetto

dolce, espressivo.

Keep thou my feet;— I do no ask to see The dis-tant scene;— one

step e - nough for me,——— one step e - nough for me.

I was not ev-er thus,—— nor pray'd——— that Thou Shouldst

lead me on; I lov'd to choose and see my path; but now, but

now, Lead Thou me on. I lov'd the gar-ish day, and spite of fears,

Pride rul'd my will, pride rul'd my will: Re-mem-ber not past

years, re-mem-ber not past years,__ re-mem-ber not,__

__ re-mem-ber not past years. So

while. And with the morn those An - gel - fac - es

smile, Which I have lov'd long since, and lost a -

while, and lost a - - while, and

lost a - while.

The Lord is my shepherd

Peter I. Tchaikovsky
Theme from Fifth Symphony
Adapted and arranged by
Richard Maxwell and Fred Feibel

Psalm 23

pas - tures,__ be - side the still wa - ters.__ He re - stor - eth my

soul:_____ he lead - eth in paths of right - eous - ness

for his name's sake.____ Tho' I walk through the val - ley_____ of the shad - ow of

death,___ I___ will fear no e - vil: for thou art

with me;_____ thy rod and thy staff___ they com-fort

me,___ thy rod and thy staff they com-fort me.___ Thou pre-par-est a

Sure - ly good - ness and mer - cy shall fol - low me all the

days of my life:_____ and __ I ____ will dwell in the house of the

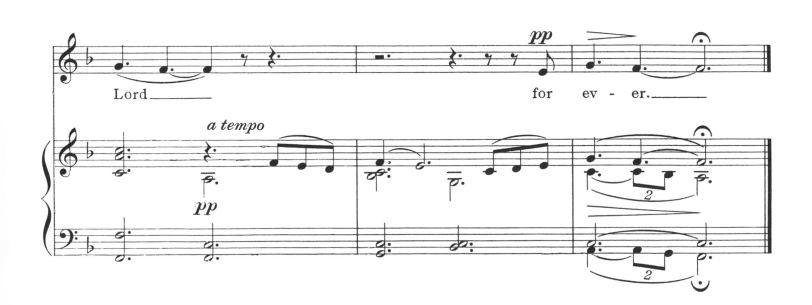

Lord_____ for ev - er._____

The Lord's Prayer

Josephine Forsyth

Give us this day our dai - ly bread. And for - give us our

Chimes

debts, as we for - give our debt - ors. And

lead us not in - to temp - ta - tion; But de - liv - er us from e - vil: For

Thine is the king-dom, and the pow-er and the glo-ry, For

ev - er and ev-er, A - men! A -

men! A - men!

„Mein gläubiges Herze, frohlocke."

"My heart ever faithful, sing praises."

JOHANN SEBASTIAN BACH.

My hope is in the Everlasting

from the cantata "The Daughter of Jairus"

John Stainer

you from the Ev-er-last-ing, our_ Sav-iour, our Sav - iour. My

hope is in the Ev-er-last-ing, that He will save you;

and joy is come un-to me

from the Ho - ly One, be-cause of the mer - cy which shall

soon come un - to you from the Ev-er-last-ing, our_ Sav-iour, our Sav -

iour.

I sent you out with mourn-ing and weep-ing, I

sent you out with mourn-ing and weep-ing. But

God will give you to me a-gain with joy___ and glad-ness, with joy___ and

glad - ness for ev - er, for ev -

Tempo Iº

hope is in the Ev-er-last-ing, that He will save you; and joy is come un-to me

from the Ho-ly One, be-cause of the mer-cy which shall soon come to

you from the Ev - er - last-ing, our Sav - iour; joy is come to

me, joy is come to me, be-cause of the mer-cy which shall soon come to

you from our Sav - iour.

My soul is athirst for God

from the cantata "The Holy City"

Alfred Robert Gaul

Repentir.

Parce domine.

O, divine Redeemer!

Prayer.

(Mezzo-Soprano, or Baritone.)

CH. GOUNOD.

Printed in the U.S.A.

166

To Mr. FRANCIS FISCHER POWERS.

O Lord, be merciful.

(Mezzo-Soprano or Baritone.)

HOMER N. BARTLETT.
Op. 96.

mer - ci - ful, O___ God, be mer - ci - ful,___

mer - ci - ful to me.

And when, redeemed from sin and hell, With all the ransomed throng I

mer - ci - ful; God___ hath been

mer - - - ci - ful,___ mer - - ci -

ful to me.

O Lord on High

Words by
Virginia P. Marwick

Music by
W. A. Mozart

*If organ is used, the editor recommends holding this chord through the three measures.

Teach us Thy right-eous-ness to share, teach us Thy

right-eous-ness to share.

Lead Thou us on thro'_ dan-gers low'r-ing, Be Thou our

shield in fears o'er - pow'r-ing; Oh, let Thy mer - cy e'er be our

guard, O - ver our life keep watch and ward, o - ver our

life__ keep watch and ward.

One Sweetly Solemn Thought

Sacred Song

Mezzo-Soprano or Baritone

PHŒBE CARY

R. S. Ambrose

I am near-er home to-day Than I've ev-er_ been be-
fore. Near-er my Fa-ther's house, Where the
man-y man-sions be; Near-er the great white
throne,_ Near-er the crys-tal sea;

Near - er the bounds of life, Where we lay our bur - dens

down; Near - er leav - ing the cross,

Near - er gain - ing the crown. But ly - ing dark - ly be -

tween, Wind - ing a - down thro' the night,

O rest in the Lord
Aria from the oratorio "Elijah"

Psalm XXXVII

Felix Mendelssohn
Edited by Carl Deis

Lord, wait pa-tient-ly for Him, and He shall give thee thy heart's de-

sires,___ and He shall give_ thee thy heart's de - sires, and He shall

give thee thy heart's de - sires. O rest in the Lord, O rest in the

Lord, and wait,_____ wait_ pa-tient-ly for Him.

" O SAVIOUR, HEAR ME! "

Offertory for Soprano or Tenor.

(with additional accompaniments *ad libitum*
for either Violin, Violoncello or Flute.)

Adaptation by Dudley Buck.

arranged from GLUCK.

1. O Sa - viour hear__ me, I ____ im - plore thee,
2. When cares of earth__ to me ____ seem hea - vy

In thee a - lone__ can peace__ be found,
Heart - sore I seek__ of thee__ re - lief,

Thou canst sus - tain and thou ____ re - store me
Thy grace re - main - eth ev - - er rea - dy

What - e'er the cares ____ that hov - - er round.
To soothe my pain, ____ to as - suage my grief.

Hear _____ my sup - - pli - ca - tion.

Turn ____ on me ____ thy lov - - ing eyes, ____ O

turn ____ on me ____ thy lov - - ing eyes;

Lord ____ I ____ long ____ for thy ____ sal - va - - tion,

And ____ would fain ____ at - - tain ____ the ____

1. prize. **2.** prize. ____ *rall.* *pp*

rall. - - - - *pp*

To Miss Alba Clawson

Out of the deep have I called unto thee

De Profundis

Psalm CXXX
according to the
Book of Common Prayer

Robert L. Bedell

thou wilt be ex-treme, to mark what is done a - miss:

O Lord, who may a - bide it? For there is mer - cy with thee:

There-fore __ shalt thou be fear - ed. I look for the Lord; my

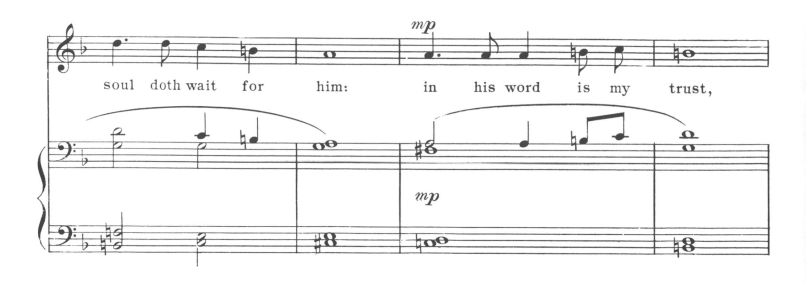

soul doth wait for him: in his word is my trust,

in his word is my trust. My soul flee-eth un - to the Lord: be -

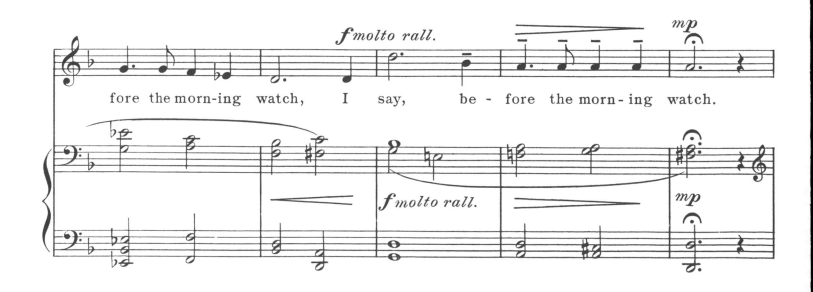

fore the morn-ing watch, I say, be - fore the morn-ing watch.

Is - ra - el, O Is - ra - el,

trust in the Lord, for with him there is mer - cy, and

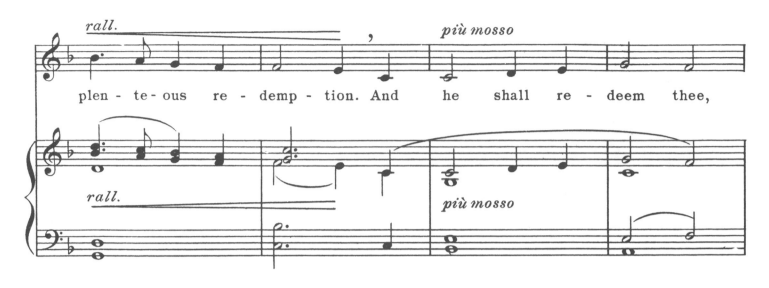

plen - te - ous re - demp - tion. And he shall re - deem thee,

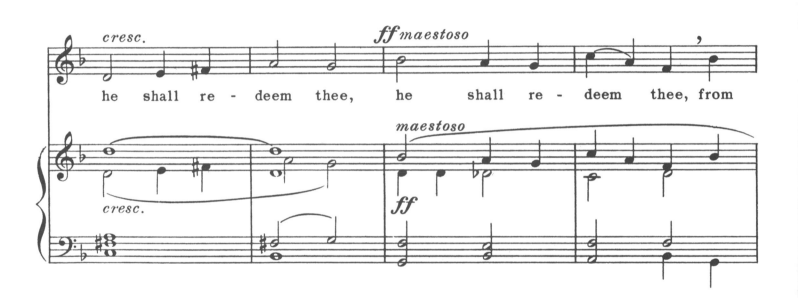

he shall re - deem thee, he shall re - deem thee, from

all, from all ___ thy sins. A - men.

The Palms

Les Rameaux

English version by
Theodore T. Barker

Jean-Baptiste Faure
Edited by Carl Deis

2. His word goes forth, and peo - ple by its might___
2. *Il a par - lé, les peu - ples à sa voix___*
3. Sing and re - joice, O blest Je - ru - sa - lem,___
3. *Ré - jou - is - toi, Sain - te Jé - ru - sa - lem,___*

Once more re - gain free - dom from de - gra - da - tion.
Ont re cou - vré leur li - ber - té per - du - e;
Of all thy sons sing the e - man - ci - pa - tion.
De tes en - fants chan - te la dé - - li - vran - ce;

p e cresc.

ff

Hu - man - i - ty doth give to each his right,___
L'hu - ma - ni - té don - ne à cha - cun ses droits,___
Through bound - less love the Christ of Beth - le - hem___
Par cha - ri - té le Dieu de Beth - lé - em___

san - - na!   Praise to the Lord!
san - - na!   *Gloi - re au Sei-gneur!*

Bless Him who com - eth to bring us sal - va -
Bé - ni ce - lui qui vient sau - ver le mon -

Tempo I°

tion!
de!

"Ring out, wild bells"

Tennyson

Ch. Gounod

Ring out the grief that saps the mind, _____ For those that here we see no more; _____ Ring out the feud of rich and poor, _____ Ring in re-dress to__ all man-kind. _____ Ring out the want, the care, the sin, _____ The faith-less cold-ness of the times. __

Suffer the little children

Mark X, 13 - 16

Ruth L. Hausman

lit - tle chil - dren to come un-to me, and for - bid_ them not: for of

such is the king-dom of God. Suf - fer the lit - tle chil-dren to come un-to

me,_ and for - bid them not, and for - bid them not: for of such_ is the

king- dom, the king-dom of God.

88640

Poco più mosso

Ver-i-ly I say un-to you, Who-so-ev-er shall not re-ceive the

king-dom of God as a lit - tle child, Who-so-ev-er shall not re-ceive the

king - dom of God as a lit - tle child, he shall not, he shall not

Tempo Io

en - ter there - in. _____ Suf-fer the lit - tle chil-dren to

come un-to me, and for-bid them not, for-bid them not: for of such is the king-dom, the king-dom of God. And he took them up in his arms, put his hands up-on them, and blessed them.

Thanks

Poem by
Raymond Garfield Dandridge*

Music by
Geoffrey O'Hara

For spread-ing plain and peak that tow'rs, We give Thee thanks. For

sun and rain and food and flow'rs, We give Thee thanks. For

* Used by special permission of the author.

cour-age and the will to do, For strength and hope and faith a-new, For

love and friend-ship strong and true, We give Thee thanks.

For

pain that serves to purge the soul, We give Thee thanks. For

cares that raise us tow'rd the goal, We give Thee thanks. For

bits of rest that in-ter-vene, For tears and sighs with smiles be-tween, For

all, O gra-cious Naz-ar-ene, We give Thee thanks. For all, O gra-cious Naz-ar-ene, We

give Thee thanks.

There is a green hill far away
Le Calvaire

CH. GOUNOD

Andante moderato

VOICE

PIANO

p

cresc.

dim.

p

There is a green hill far a-way,⏐ With-out a cit-y-wall,
Il est au loin u _ ne col-li _ ne En de _ hors de la ci _ té,

Where the dear Lord was cru - ci - fied,___ Who died to save us
Où le Sei - gneur, bon - té di - vi - ne, Mou - rut pour l'hu - ma - ni -

all.
té.

We may not know, we can - not tell, What
Et sans sa - voir, sans pouvoir dire Tout

pains He had to bear, But we be - lieve it
ce qu'il a souf - fert, Nous croy - ons que par

was for us He hung and suf - fer'd there. He
son mar - tyre Le ciel nous fût ou - vert! Il

died that we might be for-giv'n, He died to make us good,
meurt pour que Dieu nous par-donne, Oui, c'est pour nous qu'il meurt,

cresc.   dim.   p

That we might go at last to Heav'n, Sav'd by His precious blood.
Et notre cé-les - te couron-ne Est le prix de ses dou-leurs.

cresc.   dim.   p

There was no oth - er good e-nough ___ To pay the price of
Par quelle of-fran-de as-sez for-te De nos fau - tes nous la-

p   3 3

sin, He on-ly could un-lock the gate Of
rer? Lui seul du ciel pou-vait ou-vrir la

p   cresc.

These are they which came

from the cantata "The Holy City"

Alfred Robert Gaul

shine as the bright-ness of the fir-ma-ment, and as the stars, the

stars for ev - er, for ev - er and ev - er, for ev - er and

ev - er, shine_____ for ev - er and ev-er, for__

ev - er and ev - er, they shall shine____ for ev - er, shine_____

_____ for ev - er. These are

Trusting in Thee

Words and Music by
Claude L. Fichthorn

mer - cy Thy peace be - stow.

Lento

Trust - ing ev - er in Thee, Hop - ing with Thee to be.

In deep dis - tress, O God, to Thee I cry, In deep af - flic - tion, Lord,

I come to Thee.

Lento

Trust - ing ev - er in Thee, Hop - ing

with Thee to be, In deep dis - tress, O God, to Thee I cry,

In deep af - flic - tion, Lord, I come to Thee,

Ev - er trust - ing, I come to Thee.

*Chimes may be used.

The voice that breathed o'er Eden
A Wedding Song

John Keble

Homer N. Bartlett

When Jesus Walked on Galilee

Warren Charles Klein

Clara Edwards

The Worship of God in Nature
Die Ehre Gottes aus der Natur

Christian Fürchtegott Gellert
(1715 - 1769)

Ludwig van Beethoven
(1770 -1827)
Edited by Carl Deis

The heav'ns are tell-ing the Lord's end-less glo-ry, Through
Die Him - mel rüh-men des E - wi-gen Eh - re, ihr

all the earth His praise is____ found; The seas re-ech-o the mar - vel-lous
Schall pflanzt sei - nen Na - men____ fort, ihn rühmt der Erd-kreis, ihn prei - sen die

sto - ry; O man, re - peat that glo - rious sound!
Mee - re, ver - nimm, o Mensch, ihr' gött - lich Wort!